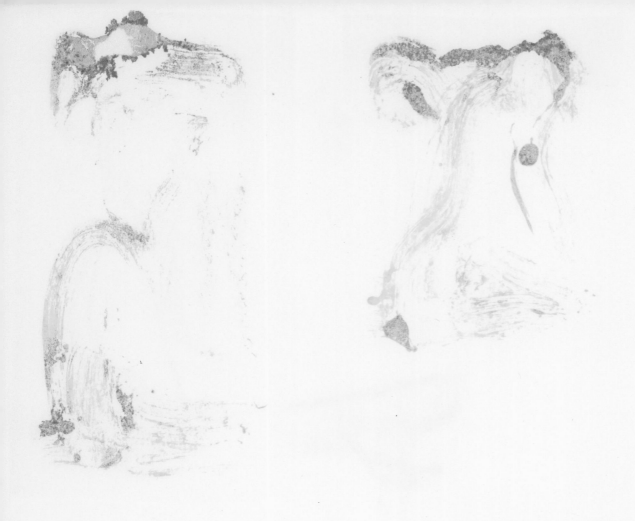

BOOKS BY ALAN DUNN:

ALAN DUNN

a portfolio of social cartoons

1957-1968

with an afterword by the author

$5.95 - Marboro $1.98 - May 1971

SIMON AND SCHUSTER · NEW YORK

Published by Simon and Schuster
Rockefeller Center, 630 Fifth Avenue
New York, N.Y. 10020

First Printing

Library of Congress Catalog Card Number: 68-8119
Manufactured in the United States of America
Printed by Mahony & Roese, New York
Bound by H. Wolff, New York

"What was the name of that tranquilizer we took?"

"*Vodka Martinis! I think they're working both sides of the street.*"

"I figure, what's it all matter? If cigarettes don't get you, radiation will."

"Remember the old days, Joe, when it was all 'Keep Off the Grass,'
'Beware of the Dog,' and stuff like that?"

"Now, it's understood that this doesn't obligate us in any way?"

"I've had it explained to me, but I still don't understand it."

*"We figured that as long as we're out to give America an inferiority complex
we might as well make it a good one."*

"Gentlemen, I don't want to be an alarmist, but what if the
next war *isn't* over in ten minutes?"

"O.K. on 'ding.' Now give me a 'dong.'"

"Do you call C-minus catching up with Russia?"

*"It was built by the Emperor Shah Jahan as a memorial to his wife.
I can just see Harry ever doing anything like that for me!"*

"All right, Dr. Heisenberg, you've finally achieved the annihilation
of matter by anti-matter. Now what?"

"Watch out for Exhibit 7-R. Poison ivy!"

"For _my_ money it's Rockefeller!"

"*Are we right for the St. Lawrence Seaway?*"

"I've been afraid of this. The people want credit cards!"

"Wouldn't you think there'd be a place between the first and second centuries where we could rest our feet?"

"Spending—uh—I mean speaking!"

"But Comrade, it's the American inflation! The ruble just doesn't buy as many top secrets as it used to."

"You can kill two birds with this one. It's good literature and it's dirty."

"Think it over. One statue sold to one museum, or a dozen fragments sold to a dozen museums."

"From now on the company wants no more excuses. We have radar, sonar, radio direction finder, autopilot, gyrocompass repeaters, and, as of today, an old salt from Gloucester."

*"I'd like you to meet Miss Tucker, who's over here on a Guggenheim; Miss Coley,
who's here on a Fulbright; and Mr. Stewart, who's on his own."*

"Which edition is this? I don't want to get stuck
with the <u>nice</u> Lady Chatterley."

"*American ship, sir. Wants to know if they can go through now, pay later.*"

"Why all the fuss? I thought they had a little pill to keep the population from exploding."

"No? What kind of an answer is 'No'?"

"We must try to think of it as progress, Ethel, not just as swish, swish, swish."

"I guess ours isn't the only planet having its troubles."

"Pardon, Monsieur l'Officier, nous sommes touristes.
Où se trouve le Tombeau de Grant?"

"Well, I can think of <u>one</u> way of stopping the drain on the dollar!"

"*Do you suppose there's something we aren't being told?*"

"_You_ brought up the subject of Berlin. _I_ was just sitting here perfectly happy!"

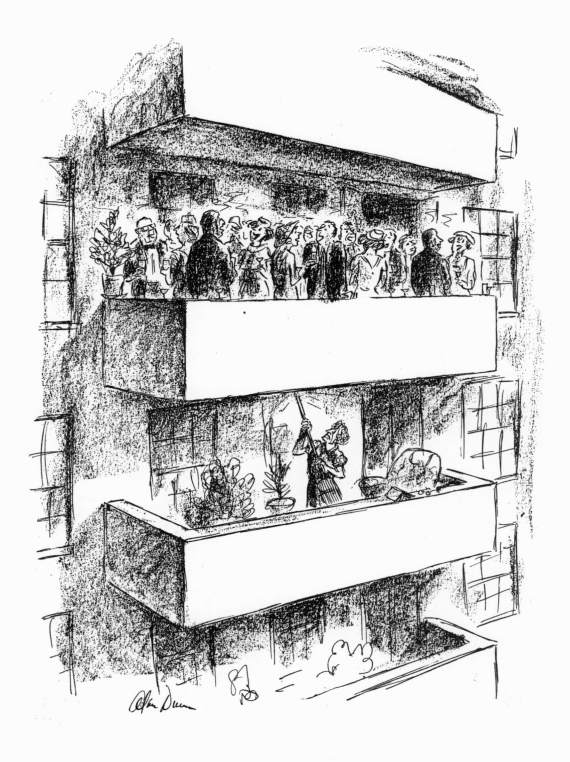

"By the way, wouldn't <u>deflation</u> also be a spiral?"

"'Extrapolation'! There's that word again!"

"Have you ever thought of being thrown open to charity?"

*"Amazing! It would take four thousand mathematicians four thousand years
to make a mistake like that!"*

"Sorry. Dr. Gove ain't in."

"Would you be interested to know that it broke all records for coast-to-coast flight?"

"Never heard of it!"

"We've really 'emerged'! Now they want us to help them with their deficit balance of payments."

"I wonder if those Tuscaroras ever stop and think how lucky
they were to have been born in America."

"Remember the good old days when there was always something to confiscate?"

"John, I've been thinking. <u>Why</u> global television?"

"*At this rate, pretty soon there won't be anything left of New York.*"

"Yummy!"

"All right, I am afraid! I'm afraid to eat, to drink, to smoke,
to drive, to fly, to breathe! And why shouldn't I be?"

"It's good to get home!"

"*You'd never know you were in New York, would you?*"

"It's worth the climb! You can see the Athens Hilton just as clear!"

"Yes, this is El Presidente—but, oh dear! I hear shots!"

"I must say it'll be good to get back to Gramercy Park,
where one has one's own key."

"Who or whom do I see about the adult English course?"

"Dichloro-diphenyltrichloroethane; lindane—gamma isomer of benzene hexachloride; isobornyl thiocyanoacetate; methoxychlor—1,1,1, trichloroethane; related terpenes; technical piperonyl butoxide; petroleum distillate; pyrethrum extract; and malathion. Or would you rather be bitten?"

"Sorry, neighbors. I just happened to lean against it."

"Where do you want Penn Station?"

"*And how is the dollar this lovely morning?*"

"Then the question is: Do we want a prosperity based on increased government spending or a prosperity based on cutting government expenses? That's where I begin not to follow."

*"First, you folks ought to familiarize yourselves with the
noises of the country. That cheep-cheep-cheep you hear now is
the refrigerator, the chirruping is the freezer, and that sort of
rumbling whump-de-whump-de-whump is the oil-burner."*

*"Just repeat to yourself: 'New York is a Summer Festival,
New York is a Summer Festival...'"*

"Before we go any further with this profit-incentive idea, I think we
should decide whether or not *we* invented it."

"*Just any kind of ribbon?*"

"Beat it!"

"I was wondering if you might stake me to a research grant
on the economics of marginal subsistence."

"My idea of Christmas is just tons and tons of money!"

*"Know something? The entire dialectic of Marxist revisionism can
be reduced to one simple formula: Money talks."*

"Another feature—it's cordless."

"Think of it <u>this</u> way. The whole world is broke,
but the United States is <u>less</u> broke."

"Well, live and learn!"

"It _can't_ be sundown, so it must be air pollution."

"You see, Daddy, this set equals all the dollars you earned; your expenses
are a sub-set within it. A sub-set of _that_ is your deductions."

"We're American imperialists and we need a drink."

"Now, when we take three hundred millilitres of a compound
containing hydrogen and oxygen in a ratio of two to one and
add three millilitres of an eight-hundredths-per-cent chlorine
solution, one millilitre of a three-ten-thousandths-per-cent
stannous-fluoride solution, and fifty millilitres of treated
industrial wastes and solids, we get drinking water."

"How much more of this is there before we come to something?"

"It's *me*—Harry!"

"*Before I begin, I'd like to make a brief statement on American foreign policy.*"

"Incredible as it may seem to those of us who live in the world of anti-matter, a mirror image exists—the reverse of ourselves—which we can only call the world of matter."

"*All right, men, you can take down those craters now.*"

HORACE
GREELEY
1811 — 1872

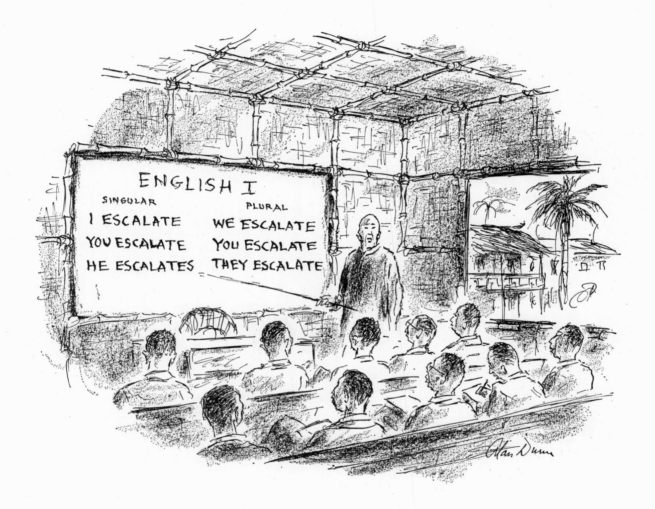

"You'll be all right in a few days. Just stay indoors, keep the windows closed,
and stop reading the New York 'Times' Air Pollution Index."

"Mind you, not their _whole_ embassy. We may want to burn it again."

"Very well. I'll run through it again quickly. You promised to
seek solutions to the problems of air pollution, mass transportation,
the water shortage, racial tensions, slum conditions, juvenile
delinquency, filthy streets, unsafe parks, traffic congestion, the
flight of industry, deficit financing, classroom shortages, and
tired thinking at City Hall."

"Then turn west from Second Avenue into Forty-ninth Street. About a hundred feet
west of Fifth, you'll come to Rockefeller Plaza. They'll know."

"I don't get it."

*"How do you decline an invitation to the White House
when you haven't been invited?"*

"I finally have it all worked out, and <u>now</u> you tell me
not to seat a hawk next to a dove!"

"Oh, come on, Louise! It's April. It's Paris. To hell with the gold
balance! Let's blow ourselves to another apéritif!"

"I'm sorry, but the Guaranteed Annual Wage is still at the verbal level."

"Chase Manhattan has to draw the line <u>somewhere</u>, Mr. Mayor!"

"He said his first words today: 'Get out of Vietnam!'"

"It's sheer, unadulterated sex, and we're all for it. Now,
to make our lawyers happy, would it cramp your style to
work in a little material of redeeming social importance?"

*"Comrade, we've just thought of another Russian first. On your fifth orbit,
you're to leave the capsule and walk the dog."*

"Don't worry. It's perfectly safe if used as directed. Just don't breathe the vapor or spraymist, avoid contact with the skin, keep the mist from your eyes, do not spray near a fire or open flame, store under a hundred and twenty degrees and out of the sun's rays, keep the can out of reach of children, and do not incinerate or puncture."

"Try and think of it as a Happening."

*"I assure you, Madam, if any such creatures as you describe really existed,
we would be the first to know about it."*

"Turn down that damn sculpture!"

"What's the Supreme Court ruling on <u>this</u>?"

"You see, Dad, Professor McLuhan says the environment that man
creates becomes his medium for defining his role in it. The
invention of type created linear, or sequential, thought, separating
thought from action. Now, with TV and folk singing, thought
and action are closer and social involvement is greater. We again
live in a village. Get it?"

"So you don't want any part of the world my generation has made? Well,
I think I can do something about that, Son."

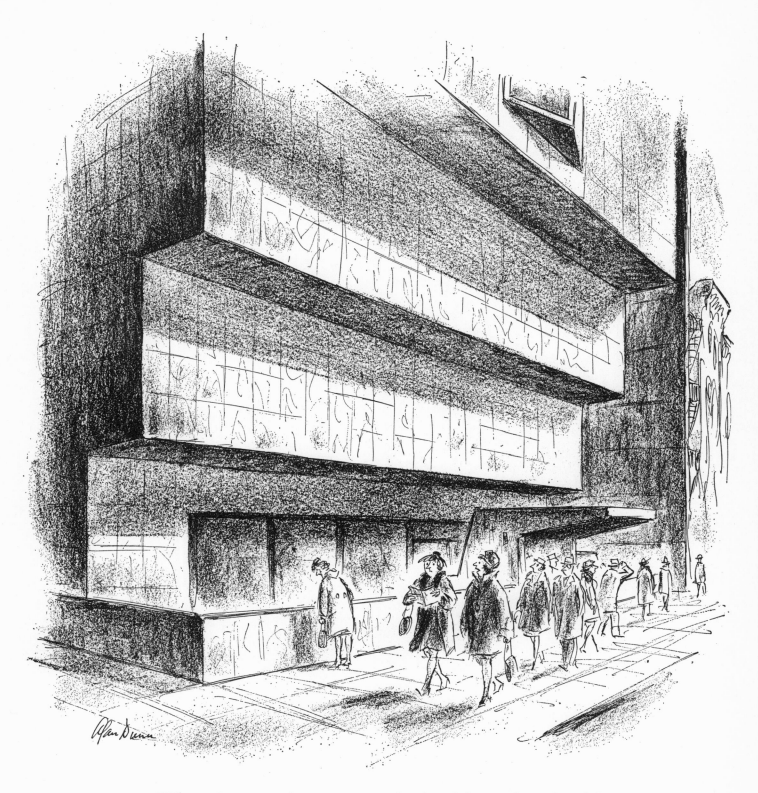

"Why can't someone design a museum that doesn't have to be explained?"

"2157836 dash 98632170053798176429763O, and reverse the charges, please."

"Leave it to the Landmarks Commission! They think of everything!"

"*Where is everybody?*"

"You might at least wait until they get here."

"I can think of a better way to avoid probate—live it up!"

"Now that they've cracked the genetic code, I suppose everyone will want to be Peabodys."

"I'd like to see Con Ed top *that*!"

"Confucius said, but Mao say."

"Nothing is wasted on basic research. We just plow all the profits back into more booze."

"It's our Oliver, calling from Wesleyan. He wants
a greater voice in something."

"...the newspapers, the TV networks, the railroads, farmers, schoolteachers,
truckers, firemen, policemen—in fact, gentlemen, the whole damn <u>world</u>
is deadlocked on the wage issue. I never thought it would end this way."

"Sniff, sniff, sniff! You've got New Jersey on the brain!"

"Think of it! Three billion people on this planet, and we found each other!"

"My first dollar. I suppose that, too, is a fake!"

"Is it all right for me to paint like Andrew Wyeth?"

"*Well, I suppose we asked for it.*"

"First, some words of our illustrious Chairman Mao."

*"Chief, they're armed with petunias, sweet William,
marigolds, and garlands of roses!"*

"Well, I don't care <u>what</u> they say about it. It's home to me."

"We hope you don't mind, but we want to show our scientists
back home a real earthling."

*"Try to cool it a bit, fellows. You don't want to give the impression
this country is divided, do you?"*

"Really! What I don't know about history would fill a library!"

"Best think tank in the country, and their conclusion after two years, thousands of dollars, and millions of words is 'God only knows!'"

"Your office won't take 'the general malaise' as an excuse."

"*I'm awfully sorry, but this is my first merger.*"

"You and your 'educated guess'!"

"You name it, we own it!"

"Would you care to know, dear, that your 'hazy morn of an enchanted day in May'
is composed of six-tenths parts per million sulfur dioxide, two parts per million
carbon monoxide, four parts per million hydrocarbons, three parts..."

GRAPHIC COMMENT ART

COMMENT ART is one of the oldest and most natural expressions of man. It is simply the statement of an idea, observation or opinion in visual form.

Although the larger field of the fine arts is replete with comment, it is, unlike comment art, primarily concerned with aesthetics—beauty, form, pattern and, more recently, dimensions beyond the everyday experiences of society.

Comment art, on the other hand, is directly involved with reality. It looks and laughs at the discrepancies between man's intentions and his realizations and, in the case of the political cartoonist, tries to improve the situation.

It has a long and varied history. Cave paintings, African sculpture and pre-Columbian figurines remain where verbal comment has vanished. With the invention of the press, comment turned graphic and with its expanded distribution became an important social and political tool, as well as a document of the life and times of one's period.

The picture has the virtue of instant cognition while the written word, as Marshall McLuhan has pointed out, requires sequential thought with a resultant lag between thought and participation. Even Tammany's Boss Tweed admitted that he little cared what was written about him since his electorate "couldn't read," but he paled at the thought of "those damned pictures," the cartoons of Thomas Nast.

Graphic comment art has three distinct divisions. There is the political cartoon, with its biting satire and its appeal to factionalism. It has recently been called the editorial cartoon but the appellative fails to define the art and merely means that "editorial cartoons" express the point of view of the vehicle in which they appear.

Then, over in the bleachers, there is comic art, usually in the form of a strip, with its breadth of reach to the masses and its happy, innocent levity in commenting on daily problems.

In the middle lies the work of the social cartoonist, whose pen is no sword but a titillating feather that reminds us constantly that we do not act as we speak or think. Since, by its very objectivity, it raises fewer hackles, its gentle approach tends to soften and ameliorate the aggravations of one's times and thereby to enlighten.

Its field of action is fixed neither on dissent nor on sheer fun. It encompasses the entire scope of the human society's activities, from pollution to pills—from technology to the desire to believe in little green men with pointed heads—and, by the use of contrast, exaggeration or stark reality, it conveys to the viewer the absurdity of going too far out in either our dreams or our fears.

Although the three categories of comment art are constant, the mood of the artist is a variable. His main directive is apparent in the course of his career but, on occasion, he can, depending on his fortunes, or perhaps because of something he ate, become angry, amused, or frolicsome as his temper demands.

In India the earliest social cartoons jocosely portrayed the deity Krishna as a Don Juan surrounded with concubines. In Egypt, especially in the tombs of Thebes, are recorded the debaucheries of those ceremonial times. There is a rather startling picture of a patrician lady who all too obviously has partaken of too much wine, and near her is a servant arriving with a ewer, giving rise to historian James Parton's caption: *Too late with the basin.*

The walls of ancient Pompeii, when uncovered, revealed many a travesty on the centurions of Rome. In the Middle Ages we have, on the capitals and walls of the churches, the most extraordinary, often revolting, caricatures of the foibles of the times.

One may wonder why the ruling classes permitted such license, but perhaps they knew that suppression only aggravated dissent, pictorial and otherwise, and that granting a reasonable latitude of expression was a safety valve that prevented an explosion. As Jefferson said, "An administration which has nothing to conceal has nothing to fear from the press," and the history of comment art shows this to be true.

As early as the thirteenth century the corrupt clergy were savagely attacked in cartoons. Later, Erasmus' "The Praise of Folly" was trenchantly illustrated by Holbein, and Brant's "Ship of Fools" owed much of its effectiveness to its drawings. Luther used every weapon in the cartoonist's arsenal in his attacks on the Pope. Although his friend Dürer restrained his pen, another, Lucas Cranach the Elder, attacked the Pope without restraint.

Wood engraving was known as early as the 1470s but the first of the broadsheet commentators was Samuel Ward of Ipswich who, in 1621, was arrested for his effronteries. The real history of the reign of Charles II lies in the broadsheets, and the ill-founded Popish Plot from 1678 to 1690 produced reams of pictorial assault. The spirit of revolt spread to art itself, and around the turn of the sixteenth century Titian expressed his contempt of the classicists by caricaturing the Laocoön as a group of monkeys.

Louis XIV inspired many a volume of graphic invective and finally, in the eighteenth century, the dam burst and pictorial satire turned from religious to political and social fields. It assailed John Law and the Mississippi Bubble and gave birth to the great master of the social cartoon, Hogarth, who battened on the dissolute habits of his period. He was both artist and writer and, like Titian, he strongly believed that works of the old masters should not take precedence over pictures that portrayed the times.

One could say that comment art is both a result and a cause. It responds to its times and in turn, by its illumination, affects the subsequent course of history. As Socrates, and later Freud, so well knew, it is not the amount of knowledge but the knowledge of *why* we act as we do that cannot but modify our actions, or reactions, for the better. The truth, as they believed, can set one free.

Under Louis XVI and Marie Antoinette comment art became political. In England, the prolific Gillray attacked the court of George III and reviled Fox, although he was kind to Burke. The "Fourberies de Femmes" was Gavarni's angry answer to the morality of the women of France, while in England the well-bred, gentler sex inspired Cruikshank and Leech more toward social satire. Although Napoleon allowed no caricature, his hand could not reach across the Channel and stay the pen of Gillray who, in a widely circulated picture, portrayed him as the Gingerbread Baker of Kings.

It was Louis Philippe's reign that spawned the famed *Le Charivari*, edited by Charles Philipon and his stable of "six poor artists," one of whom was Daumier. The latter reconstructed the king in the form of a pear, which soon became a symbol. When *Le Charivari* became known as "the stronger party" the artists soon found themselves cooling their heels in a six-month imprisonment, as might have been expected. Cham and Gavarni also drew for *Le Charivari*, but as their attacks were more social than political, they fared better.

As the times became less brutal in the nineteenth century, the satire became milder. Doré, who drew for the *Journal pour Rire*, soon turned to illustration. The German periodical *Fliegende Blätter* reflected only the *Gemütlichkeit* of its day. Goya, in Spain, raised his voice and pen against the Peninsular War but in Italy only the verbal witticisms of Pasquino—from whom "pasquinades"—contributed to the political scene.

The real growth of the social cartoon came with the birth of *Punch* in England in 1841. The pictorial comments of John Leech, Richard Doyle, John Tenniel, George Du Maurier and others are famous. Probably the most popular of all social cartoons was Du Maurier's picture of the Right Reverend host inquiring of the young curate who was his guest at the dinner table as to whether his egg was bad, and the curate's embarrassed response, "Oh no, My Lord, I assure you, parts of it are excellent!"

The English social scene was further illuminated by the boisterous work of Rowlandson around the turn of the nineteenth century, to be followed by a long period of masterful pen-and-ink artists from Phil May, Frank Reynolds, Ernest Shepard and H. M. Bateman to the contemporary Rowland Emett and Ronald Searle. In more political aspects Beerbohm, Bairnsfather and especially Low sustained the great tradition.

The first great American caricaturist, in both pen and pencil, was Benjamin Franklin, who, in his brother James's paper, the *New England Courant*, took sharp aim at Cotton and Increase Mather. Again history repeats and James landed in prison while Benjamin took over until the Mathers drove him to Philadelphia. His design for the Franklin Cent of 1787 with "We Are One" on one side and "Mind Your Business" on the other was typical of his comment.

After Franklin, cartooning became chiefly political. In 1811 in the *Boston Centinel*, Gilbert Stuart, the painter, created on a map of Massachusetts the celebrated Gerry-mander as a reproof to Governor Gerry who, not altogether of his own will, had redistricted the state on political rather than geographical grounds.

Following the War of 1812, Jefferson's Era of Good Feeling gave birth to no great cartoons of dissent, but later on, that partisan of the Civil War, Thomas Nast, created the series of magnificent political cartoons that finally toppled the Tweed Ring in New York City.

After Nast, the cartoonists surrendered their political role for that of social satire as the times became more stable and prosperous. Humor was to become America's greatest contribution to world folk culture. The comic strip spread far beyond our borders, and eventually Walt Disney circled the globe with Mickey Mouse.

In social cartooning Charles Dana Gibson, on the old *Life*, was no Gavarni with his vicious attacks on women, but the creator of a moral, ideal but sharp-witted Gibson Girl. After a great period of graphic commentators, such as A. B. Frost, Peter Newell, Oliver Herford, W. E. Hill, Art Young, and the painters John Sloan, Boardman Robinson and Walt Kuhn, the cartoon began to decline until *The New Yorker* appeared on the scene in 1925, and a new era of social cartooning was born.

Although *The New Yorker* did not invent the one-line caption, it printed little else, and this succinct, literate approach to the social scene soon dominated the entire world of graphic social-comment weeklies. Whether the magazine's success stemmed from its sophisticated editing or from its stable of spirited artists, or was a response to the collective unconscious that knew, despite a 1929 depression, that an era of unparalleled material and scientific achievement lay ahead, is impossible to know. For where there is demand there is supply, and *The New Yorker* may have merely mirrored that surge of confusion and growth.

GRAPHIC COMMENT ART by its very directness is one of the most effective statements of man. The child of today who surreptitiously draws an awkward caricature of "teacher" on the blackboard may be, if the times to come warrant it, another Hogarth or Nast.

However, since political cartooning fades with a decline in tyranny, it might be conceivable that if human perfectibility were ever to become a reality the social and comic cartoon would also disappear by lack of any further contrast between aim and achievement.

The ensuing paradise, if one could call it that, would be a world without laughter.

ALAN DUNN

ABOUT THE ARTIST

THE SOCIAL CARTOONIST *represented in this collection makes no claim to any special distinction in the great history of comment art. He regards himself primarily as a workhorse in a medium to which he is dedicated.*

He early abandoned the partisanship of the political cartoon for the social approach, not just because he believed that the former tended to polarize rather than convert the opposition, but because he deeply felt that, irrespective of party labels, all people were an extraordinary mixture of true virtue and pure human cussedness—a Yin and Yang that, when assembled, might create a syncretic oneness in this divided world.

In line with his belief that the social cartoonist should be a commentator and not just an illustrator, all of his captions and his ideas are his own.

He is a complete New York Stater. Both of his parents were born in Schoharie County, New York, and although he himself happened to be born in Belmar, New Jersey, on August 11th, 1900 (Belmar having been his parents' summer home), he was and is essentially a lifetime resident of New York City.

In 1926 he sold his first drawing to The New Yorker, *and so embarked on his true career. In 1936 he was invited to draw a monthly comment cartoon for the* Architectural Record. *It provided him with an outlet for his love of all things structural as well as an opportunity to point out in an amiable way the many times that form has disastrously failed to follow function.*

In addition to four cartoon collections, he is the author of two prose-and-picture books, East of Fifth *and* Is There Intelligent Life on Earth? *He also collaborated with Eric Hodgins on a prose-picture history of the American businessman called* Enough Time? *His work has been exhibited nationally and internationally and he is represented in a number of museums and manuscript collections.*

For the more than two thousand contributions of his that were published in The New Yorker, *the hundreds in the* Architectural Record *and the thousands in other publications, he has nothing but gratitude in having been allowed a voice, however quiet, in the graphic comment of an incredible century.*